J'ai emmené la Lune se promener
I Took the Moon for a Walk

Written by Carolyn Curtis
Illustrated by Alison Jay

French translation by Annie Arnold

I took the Moon for a walk last night.
It followed behind like a still summer kite,

J'ai emmené la Lune se promener la nuit dernière.
Elle m'a suivi comme un cerf-volant immobile,

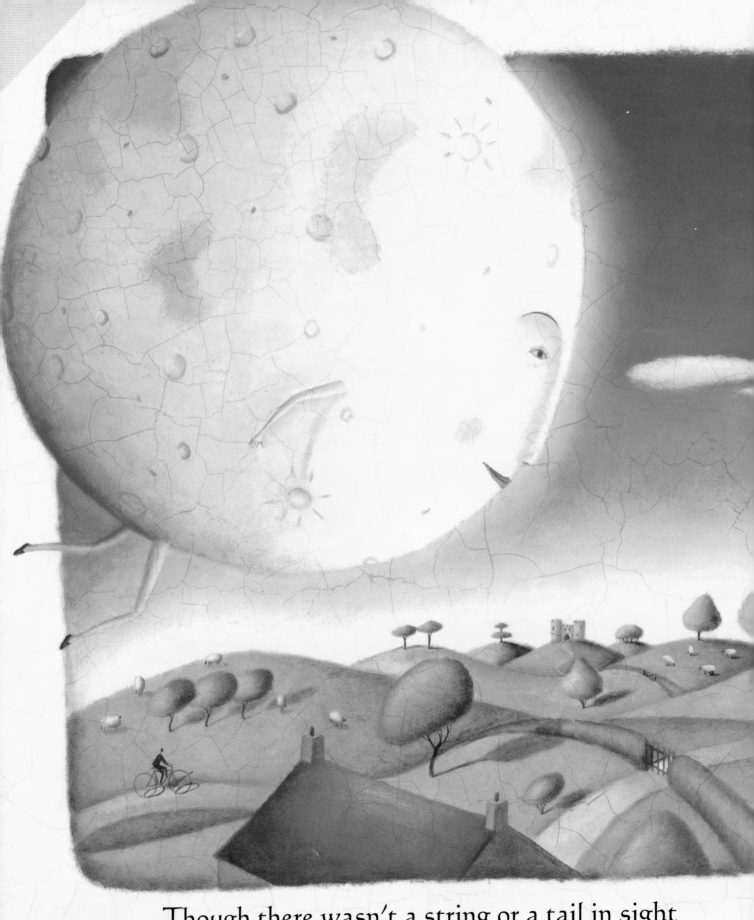

Though there wasn't a string or a tail in sight
when I took the Moon for a walk.

Bien qu'il n'y ait pas de ficelle ou de queue visible
quand j'ai emmené la Lune se promener.

I carried my blue torch just in case
the Moon got scared and hid its face.

J'ai emporté ma torche bleue au cas où
la Lune aurait peur et cacherait son visage.

Mais elle a jeté un coup d'œil à travers
les nuages qui étaient
délicats comme de la dentelle
Quand j'ai emmené la Lune se promener.

But it peeked through clouds
that were fragile as lace
When I took the Moon for a walk.

I warned the Moon to rise a bit higher
so it wouldn't get hooked on a church's tall spire,

J'ai prévenu la Lune de monter un peu plus haut
pour qu'elle ne s'accroche pas au clocher de l'église,

While the neighbourhood dogs made a train-whistle choir
when I took the Moon for a walk.

Pendant que les chiens du voisinage aboyaient en choeur
quand j'ai emmené la Lune se promener.

We tiptoed through grass where the night crawlers creep
when the rust-bellied robins have all gone to sleep,

Nous avons marché sur la pointe des pieds
là où les insectes nocturnes rampent
quand tous les rouges-gorges sont partis se coucher,

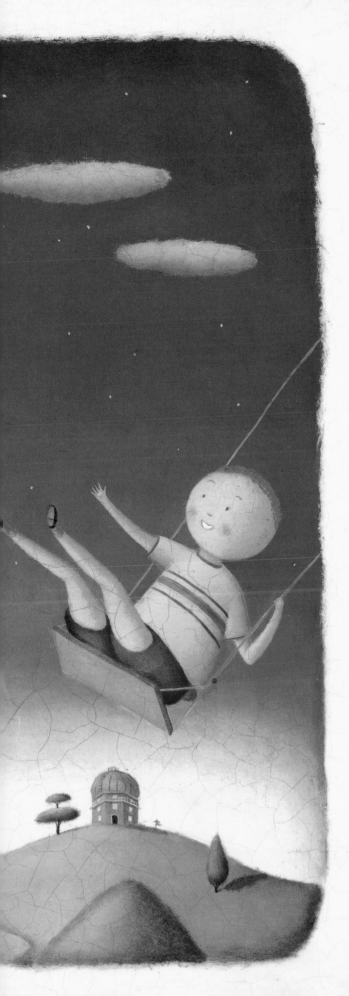

Nous avons fait la course jusqu'aux
balançoires où j'ai donné des coups
de pied très haut
Et imaginé que la Lune me demandait
de voler,

We raced for the swings,
where I kicked my feet high
And imagined the Moon had
just asked me to fly,

Hand holding hand through the starry night sky
when I took the Moon for a walk.

Main dans la main à travers la nuit étoilée
quand j'ai emmené la Lune se promener.

We danced 'cross the bridge where the smooth waters flow.
The Moon was above and the Moon was below,

Nous avons dansé en traversant le pont où les eaux fluides coulent.
La Lune était au-dessus et la Lune était en dessous,

Et éclairé par les deux j'ai reçu leur lueur
Quand j'ai emmené la Lune se promener.

And bright in between them
I echoed in their glow
When I took the Moon for a walk.

Then as we turned back, the Moon kept me in sight.
It followed me home and stayed there all night,

Puis quand nous sommes retournés, la Lune me surveillait.
Elle m'a suivi jusque chez moi et est restée là toute la nuit,

And thanked me by sharing its sweet sleepy light
when I took the Moon for a walk.

Et m'a remercié en partageant sa douce lumière endormie
quand j'ai emmené la Lune se promener.

The Mysterious Moon

What do you see when you look at the moon? Children who live in Europe and the United States imagine that they see a man when they look at the moon. Children in Japan and India see a rabbit, and children in Australia see a kitten. But all children, no matter where they live, look up in wonder at the same moon.

The moon is primarily made of rock with a small iron core. It creates no light of its own, but reflects sunlight.

The shape of the moon seems to change during the month because the sunlight strikes the moon at different angles as it travels through space. These shapes are called 'phases'. Here are some of the phases of the moon:

New Moon   *Crescent Moon*   *Half Moon*   *Gibbous Moon*   *Full Moon*

When the moon is growing larger in the sky, we say that it is 'waxing'. When it is growing smaller, we say that it is 'waning'.

For people all over the world, the moon has always been an important way to measure time. Although the solar calendar has become the standard international way of doing this, many people still use lunar, or moon, calendars.

The moon can be a friend to farmers and gardeners - those who follow tradition know that the best time to sow seeds and transplant young shoots is when the moon is waxing.

Moon festivals are celebrated in many societies. The Chinese Moon Festival is held during the Harvest Moon - the full moon that rises in mid-autumn.

Many Celtic and Native American festivals are also held at the time of the Harvest Moon, when the people give thanks for the harvest and for all living things on earth.

The World at Night

If you took the moon for a walk through your neighbourhood, what would you show it? What would you hear, and what would you see?

Wherever you are, you would probably see some nocturnal creatures - mammals, birds and insects that usually sleep during the day and come out at night. They are especially adapted to life under the moon and stars:

Cats have eyes that see very well in the dark.

Rabbits have large ears that capture sound across long distances.

Bats use sounds and echoes to help them fly safely and find food.

Fireflies light up at night so that they can find each other.

Owls have necks that can turn right around and huge, flat eyes that enable them to see other creatures that are far away.

Some flowers are nocturnal too. They bloom and release their fragrance after dark.

And although you are asleep during the night, your mind is not! During the day, your waking, or conscious, mind is active, but when you sleep, your dreaming, or unconscious, mind is busy. So, the world at night is not so quiet as it seems!

For my nephew Christopher, *who first walked with the moon*
and my mother Estella, *who held his hand*
For my father Harold, *the star we steer by*
and Lucan, *my sun*
and, of course, for Emilie, *for Everything* - C.C.

The author extends heartfelt thanks to the society of Children's Book Writers and Illustrators for generous support in the form of
a Barbara Karlin Grant, WarmLines Parent Resources, Jane Yolen, the Jeff Kelly and Newton Library Critique Groups, and Alison Keehn.

For Mark, happy moon walking, love from Alison.

Mantra Lingua TalkingPEN
Global House
303 Ballards Lane
London N12 8NP
www.mantralingua.com
www.talkingpen.co.uk